Hello, Winter!

written by Suzanne Martinucci
illustrated by Bruce Armstrong

McGraw-Hill
School Division

New York   Farmington

It was winter.

Kim saw snow in our wagon.

It was winter.

Tom saw frost on the window.

It was winter.

There was ice on the trees.

It was winter.

Tom was cold in the snow.

It was winter.

There was wood in the fire.

It was winter.

It was warm in our house.

It was winter.
It was a wonderful time!